Doing it in Wellies

For my family

First published in the UK in 2014
by Middle Farm Press

British Library Cataloguing-in-Publication Data
A catalogue record for this book is available from the British Library
ISBN 978-0-9928896-0-9

Editor: Kate Taylor
Designer: Kath Grimshaw
Photographer: Richard Hammerton
Illustrations by Peter Troop
Old Press font by Galdino Otten

Printed in Italy by L.E.G.O S.p.A.
Published by Middle Farm Press
www.middlefarmpress.com

Doing it in Wellies

SAM GRAY

Introduction

According to my Oxford English Dictionary, a smallholding is 'an agricultural holding smaller than a farm'. While that may be true, for me running a smallholding is a reality check – it is about quality of life, living by the seasons, working and connecting with nature, nurturing animals for food and eggs and, best of all, growing more vegetables than you will ever be capable of eating.

Unless you are born into this lifestyle, becoming a smallholder takes time and practice. It is definitely something you evolve into, almost without realising. The understanding that you are the custodians of a sizeable plot of land takes several months to come to terms with, then only a few more after that to realise you could do with three times the amount of space. Christmas presents change from classy clothes to boiler suits; expensive wellies become a worthwhile investment as shoes become obsolete.

By the time friends are picking straw out of your hair mid-conversation, you find bailing twine and a pocketknife in every coat pocket, and your 'once in a blue moon' manicure starts with the filing of your hands, you know! You know you've shovelled enough muck, fed enough animals, witnessed enough births and deaths, fixed enough fences, sown enough seeds, planted enough trees, picked enough fruit, made enough jams, pickles and cordials, nurtured enough veg and learned enough about land management to finally consider yourself worthy of the title 'smallholder'.

If someone had told me a decade ago that I'd be writing a book about life on a smallholding, I would have laughed disbelievingly while eyeing up my company car and laptop. A decade before that, I doubt I even knew what one was!

I grew up in a village outside St. Albans in a somewhat quieter Hertfordshire during the 1970s and 1980s, and although I enjoyed an outdoor childhood, it was by no means preparation for keeping chickens and shovelling pig muck.

My 'education' in countryside ways started the moment I met my husband. His passion for nature, wildlife and dangerous aerobatic sports had me transfixed from the minute we met.

In the 1-acre garden surrounding our cottage in the middle of a 1500-acre shooting estate he taught me how to shoot for the pot, set rat traps, use a chainsaw, erect wire fencing and skin a rabbit. By the time I was capable of herding escaped cows off the lawn we knew we made an excellent team.

After nearly ten years of our 'good life' in miniature, the initiation was over. It was time to move on. Middle Farm was waiting for us whether we were ready or not.

Chapter One

We Bought a Smallholding!

Only just. Late and lost for our viewing, we almost turned back home. After miles of unfamiliar winding lanes and farmland we stumbled across the local pub. Since the farm had been there for nearly 600 years it was likely that someone could point us in the right direction. Tucked away on the north-east slopes of Shropshire's Long Mynd, we finally arrived at Middle Farm.

Sliding gently into the drive as we negotiated more snow and ice than the county had seen in years, we gave each other that knowing look. It was perfect; nothing too grand or too rustic. The tour of the house confirmed our instincts as we climbed one small staircase, came down another, ducked through a four-foot doorway and gazed with wonder at the stunning, white, snow-covered gardens outside. Our minds racing with ideas, we decided to hike around the land. With a one-year-old stuffed into a backpack and a three-year-old just marginally taller than the snow,

we climbed to the top of the highest field. The breathtaking view that faced us as we finally reached the hilltop heightened our desire to buy the farm. It ticked all the boxes on our checklist – plenty of acres, streams, woodland, grazing, sheds, even a well-stocked fishing lake – and it could provide us with a source of revenue.

There was one catch… for five days a week I was going to have to do it alone. With young children to support, we needed my husband's income to live day-to-day and generate more savings – I needed to prove that we could live without it before he could join me full time. Being responsible for cultivating a new way of life, and a sustainable one for our family, would come with enormous challenges.

Middle Farm had to evolve and I had more to learn than I could have possibly imagined.

On our first night up here in the Church Stretton hills, I clearly remember lying in bed and feeling somewhat humbled by my surroundings. The enormous medieval cruck frames that were (and still are) miraculously holding the centre of the house together conjured up thoughts of what it must have been like for the men who built this house with ropes and pulleys. Admiring their work nearly 600 years later, from the comfort of a memory-foam mattress and seven-tog duck down duvet, made me feel extremely fortunate – and at the same time, woefully inadequate.

This old farmhouse was definitely made of tough stuff. Bigger than a cottage, smaller than a traditional farmhouse, we were captivated by its quirky and enchanting rustic beauty – a hotchpotch of add-ons throughout the centuries had somehow merged into one. The latest addition had apparently been made during the 18th century, but the centre of the house originated with the monks attached to

Haumond Abbey during the 1400s. It had been constructed with an assortment of oak beams, and to this day still boasts a superbly spacious inglenook fireplace that, during the winter, keeps us, and all those who visit, warm. It was rumoured that the room I now call my study once housed a dairy cow for the daily milk supply. Not sure how that would work today? There is a limit to my love of farm animals and a cow in the house is a long way past it! No doubt this jumble of buildings had been a lot of things to many different people throughout the centuries. Now it was to be our home and the central hub of our new adventures.

The size of the farm outbuildings seemed overwhelmingly huge at first. How were we ever going to find the time or need to fill two 100ft-long modern-day cattle sheds? They are enormous buildings dominating much of the yard's surface area. Constructed of giant breeze blocks, steel supports, weathered wooden slated sides and corrugated roofs, they are incredibly strong. I remember wanting to take them down initially because I thought they were ugly – that would have been a huge mistake!

We were also the new owners of a slightly rickety and patched-up World War I Dutch barn, a 15th century stone byre and a beautiful but unused old granary building. The total storage space is several times that of our house. The front yard and driveway is set in a U-shape with the house in the middle and the 15th century holiday cottages either side. In a previous life the cottages had housed many cows, sheep and fodder but when 'Foot and Mouth' hit the UK they were sympathetically restored into beautiful guest accommodation to bring in a different source of income to the farm. For practicality reasons, it is perfectly formed. Nothing is too far away. Saying that, I've lost plenty of weight and saved thousands on gym membership running between buildings.

Prior to our purchase, the farm had nearly 400 stunning acres of land on the north-east slopes of the Long Mynd, roughly four miles from Church Stretton. The previous owners had used this mainly for grazing cattle and/or sheep, hence the enormous cattle shed. Our procurement was lot number one, which included the house, all of the outbuildings and 32 acres consisting of 7 acres of new woodland, a 2.5-acre fishing lake, streams, grazing and plenty of mature wooded areas to keep us in firewood for life. High on a hill, it is surrounded by a network of interweaving narrow lanes and is one of the few places in the UK where you have to stop to let wild ponies cross. At just under 1000ft above sea level, which is 200ft above the snow line, we made a great choice buying my very elderly 4x4 Mitsubishi Shogun before we moved in. She is never clean and shudders at the thought of 80mph, but handles snow conditions with ease and (in my opinion) far better than any modern-day car with a snow drive button.

For years before moving, we read a variety of husbandry books, smallholder magazines, gardening encyclopaedias and manuals. Like many others, we had created two full-to-bursting folders with the very original titles of 'smallholding ideas'. These were crammed with cut-out magazine articles that were of particular interest, estimated costs of living, savings needed to survive (this was thrown away fairly quickly!) and well-researched activities that could make us money.

Every option was there, from rearing goats for meat to keeping bees for honey. The latter idea was scrubbed as my husband finally announced, after he'd bought me a book on the subject and promised me a beekeeping course for Christmas, that he had an allergic reaction to bee stings. Here was our opportunity to put our research to good use – 32 acres of our own beautiful countryside was nothing if not inspiring.

With holiday guests in mind, as well as our own love of the 'aesthetically pleasing', the ideas came quickly to make the concrete area around the farm greener, the cattle sheds tidier, and to expand and create growing plots for edible gardens. The possibilities for a smallholding were endless. We wasted no time in applying for a Council Parish Holding (CPH) number, which would allow us to have livestock on the farm. We spent hours, if not days, learning about and applying for various stewardship schemes and grants. Little did we realise that by

not cutting the hedges for three years we could probably account for the largest UK population of hedge sparrows!

There was an enormous amount to take in and consider, but with the television off, the fire lit and bottles of Bordeaux in plentiful supply, we spent many an evening planning. Our excitement outweighed any underlying fears of failure. It had to work, our passion and commitment were such that there was no other option.

Chapter Two

Getting Stuck In

Way before any realities of livestock, vegetable growing or even the purchase of pretty chickens, there were basic things we had to put right or research before going any further. We'd have to learn about our land and lake and think carefully about how best to use our outbuildings.

The storage space that we found so overwhelmingly large in the beginning started to get rather full. In true smallholding style my husband insisted that one of our first purchases should be a tractor. I think he was more concerned that if he didn't get one immediately, other priorities would take over and funds wouldn't allow for one at all!

A farm of any size without a well-used Massey Ferguson sitting in the shed is, of course (according to him), not worthy of the title 'farm'. The list of 'must have' equipment has a habit of growing. On top of the tractor (not literally of course) we've added stock trailers, normal trailers, tipper trailers, log splitters, fencing and numerous materials. Space for actual farm animals would have to be considered later. Opportunities to buy good second-hand equipment don't always come up when you need them. Strong and secure outbuildings are imperative. Farms with lots of modern and expensive equipment (even second-hand) are prime targets for the knowledgeable thief. Although house break-ins are rare around this part, we learned from previous experience that bolting your ride-on lawn mower to the floor is not considered extreme.

Deciding to continue a longstanding contract with a neighbour to house a few very handsome Shire Horses in one half of our cattle sheds was a welcome addition to the farm. These beautiful animals would attract a great deal of interest from our guests, especially when they were being prepared for competition or cart pulling. It also offers a little revenue that helps towards the maintenance of the sheds and outbuildings.

Another immediate source of income came from a neighbouring sheep farmer who rents some of the grazing land. Since we were not in a position to use it straight away, it seemed a clear solution to keep the grass down to a manageable level. He is one of the finest farmers we could have hoped to meet, let alone have the fortune to live next door to. His experience has aided enormously with many of the jobs that require a helping hand. Pulling our tractor out of the quagmire near the lake, twice in the first year, was particularly embarrassing but he never laughed or made comment. Smallholding does not mean 'doing it on your own', far from it, learning from others is invaluable and enriching.

While his sheep did their part on the grass, we had the opportunity to invest more time in other areas. We knew enough to recognise that the relationship between any smallholder and their land is fundamental to how well either one thrives. The seasons change quickly and if you're not watching, the opportunities to nurture, harvest and make good can easily turn into undesirable responsibilities.

When we first moved here, we imagined taking a flask of coffee down to the edge of the stream and sitting while the children enjoyed getting soaked. One of the first hot summer days we had, clad just in their pants (the children – not me), we excitedly made our way down to the stream… only to find that it had all but disappeared. It was a trickle at best. Not quite the dam-making experience we imagined. By the time it was a fun torrent again, nobody fancied staying long enough to drink coffee let alone strip down to their underwear. On a more serious note, the lack of water in summer could not be ignored. The land is constantly changing which comes hand in hand with new lessons to be learned.

'Getting stuck in' is an apt title when it comes to much of our land during autumn and winter. Tractors buried in mud up to their windows are not as uncommon as you might imagine.

Another lesson was learned through an old and well-known rhyme:

Cut thistles in May, they'll grow in a day
Cut them in June, that is too soon
Cut them in July, then they will die

Although I'm not sure how accurate that is, we seem to be cutting them out from the same spot every July! As for the molehills, they are a blight on the landscape and an unpleasant reminder that sheep are not the only ones living in the fields. Experience also prompts us to batten down the cattle shed doors in high winds (best remembered by early evening, not three o'clock in the morning) and collect plenty of kindling in the summer (far less stressful than rummaging around in a wet wood in winter).

The real fun began with the investment in skiwear. While skiing is possible in the hills, the shortage of chairlifts in Shropshire makes it fairly heavy work. Tobogganing, on the other hand, is exhilarating to the extreme. The risk of careering into barbed-wire fencing only makes the downhill race one of uncontrollable laughter followed by a deliberate tumble to safety. There have to be some advantages to living above the snow line and there is no doubt in my mind (or those that visit) that decent snow is one of them.

We learned quickly that temperatures are always at least two degrees colder than the lowlands and the fishing lake can freeze to more than five-inches thick when it drops below minus ten degrees. On our first winter here we braved ice-skating (in wellies not skates) on the lake. Admittedly it was in the shallows, no more than a foot deep, but we scared ourselves to death when we united in a jump to try and break the ice. The trapped air below travelled across the lake and was released on the other side, making the loudest and eeriest deep echoing sound we had ever heard. We couldn't agree on whether it was a giant burping carp or a sea monster but we ran and skidded, clutching at each other and screaming with laughter (and a little bit of terror), back to the house.

The stream that replenishes the lake represents the most spirited element of the farm – ever-changing, eroding, flooding and occasionally drying out. It keeps the sheep in drinking water and nourishes the hundreds of elderly trees that grow alongside its banks.

There are a couple of walks across the land that meander through our streams and wooded areas, including a trip around the spectacularly calming lake, ending with views from the top of 'Sunny Bank' at approximately 1200 feet. It doesn't take long to walk around 32 acres but the scene changes daily depending on the light, weather and, of course, season. The peace, quiet and high perspective often inspire new initiatives. The two most-heard phrases in our house are: "I'm just going for a walk in the wilds", referring, usually, to a trip beyond Sunny Bank to the new and constantly transforming woodland, as well as, "I've had an idea!"

The woodland is the source of many good ideas. My husband is very passionate about wood and woodland – everything from coppicing and clearing fallen trees to splitting logs and stoking the fire. Just as well, the mature trees surrounding the lake and streams will give up enough firewood to keep us warm for years. With every trip around the land he gets more excited about starting his own log selling business;

impossible to fit in with a full-time job but it's nice to dream. It is, at least, worth making sure that the trees are properly managed so there is something to coppice in the future. My only request to him is that chainsaw accidents are limited to the one and only incident that has already been. Appearing at the conservatory doors with blood pouring down his face was enough to send me into a full-blown faint. Moments later I heard the words "I'm alright, just a bit dizzy. I fell off the ladder and the chainsaw hit my head…" then a pause, followed by "…are you alright to drive me to A&E?" A whopping 22 stitches later, we came to terms with three things – I am totally useless with shock and gushing blood, not strapping the ladder to the tree was a really bad idea and we needed a better first-aid box.

His wealth of experience with a chainsaw, and subsequent protective gear, has kept him safe since but it was a sobering reminder to pay attention. Rolling countryside usually means hospitals are far away and large plots of land can often mean you're on your own. Two-way radios are an excellent investment if there's a signal – we're not that lucky.

The 7-acre newly-planted wood just above our top field was already three years old when we moved in. Thousands of saplings had been planted, a mix of Larch, Alder, Horse Chestnut, Oak, Ash, Willow, Spruce, and Beech. There was no obvious growth for a few years. It takes that long for the roots to establish and take hold. But we watched the little saplings grow and eventually tower above our heads. They have indeed become trees. Someone else had done all the hard work planting them and now it would need managing. Woodland management on this scale is very good for a marriage. Gone for the day with a packed lunch, strimmer, chainsaw, safety helmet, goggles and protective trousers, I know he'll be in his element and return at dusk, covered in sawdust with at least two blackthorn splinters to show for all the effort. Who needs a shed when you can escape to the country? Enlisting the occasional help of a local woodsman was also a wise idea – and he would be much less likely to pass out at the sight of blood.

These woods are home to thousands of creepy crawlies, badgers, foxes, birds of prey and many unseen others, they are relatively untouched and have a slightly wild beauty about them despite being deliberately planted. Watching the leaves and the needles of the larch change colour throughout the seasons is one of the great pleasures of living here, and as it matures and becomes hardy it is also the brainstorm for future livestock and wildlife opportunities.

Learning about course fishing was an unexpected angle on running our smallholding. My only experience of fishing was hours of childhood boredom being told repeatedly by my otherwise very loving father "be quiet, you'll disturb the fish". Skimming stones and splashing around in the streams with my kid sister was enough to send him into apoplectic rage. We weren't invited to the river very often.

He did try to excite a love of fly fishing by teaching me to cast as if by the river. We were in the garden at the time and the only thing I caught was an apple in the tree behind. I was young and I didn't understand the patience needed, but whether fishing for trout and salmon or carp and orfe, I do now understand the attraction of peace and quiet.

The lake is calming and packed with wildlife. It had been dug out to a maximum 18-feet deep two decades before we took over. The owners had carefully stocked it with various species of carp, golden orfe and tench. Regular fishermen seem to relish spending a day or more sitting in little chairs, inside little tents sweighed down by a multitude of kit, on the topped grass that surrounds the lake. Occasionally, they are rewarded with rare sightings of a hen harrier or kingfisher (possibly the most exciting event of the day)! Otters, although magnificent to watch,

are not welcome guests. They can eat all the fish in a lake the size of ours in the space of a few weeks. Visits are luckily infrequent so stocks are not noticeably affected, and while fishermen are there, they (the otters) are not quite brave enough to risk helping themselves. Neither of us had ever seen a gooseander before, so it was a great surprise to learn that what we thought were beautiful-looking ducks were in fact razor-billed thieves that ate baby fish. On looking them up further, neither could we believe that they docked on Middle Farm fishing lake! Since they are also protected, there's not much we can do except have regular 'scare the gooseanders off the lake' visits throughout their three or four week stay. This entails a quick walk to and around the lake making stupid noises until they fly off to find somewhere else to rest.

We have come to know some wonderful guests who have stayed at the cottages and fished here for more years than they care to remember. Greeting them back to the farm is like getting together with old friends as we enjoy the annual ritual of a great barbeque, lots of red wine and a late night – or at least until 10pm. The four o'clock morning start (for them) as they make their way to the fishing lake puts pains to anything later! Their party of three has sadly become two after the passing of a great team mate. Never to be down for long, they maintained their infectious sense of humour by naming the irritating swan that lands on the lake during their visits after him. Brian the swan! How he would have laughed.

Extraordinarily, after a full week of fishing, two pub meals, cornflakes for breakfast and a well-kept diary of every fish landed (or not as the case may be) they return home refreshed and revitalised.

We made the decision not to advertise the lake as a fishery since we're not always around to manage it as such; consequently the revenue from the lake could be much greater. As it stands, it just about covers the costs of upkeep – hiring a digger to clear the silt trap in the incoming stream; the chainsaw fuel used to coppice and manage the rapidly growing alder and willow on the banks; and annual restocking of young fish to put back whatever the gooseanders, otters or herons have taken out.

As well as the stream replenishing the lake we are lucky enough to have our own spring that supplies all water to the house, cottages and four other local properties. The main source happens to be on our land and is free to those who are connected. The water is free, the treatment is not. We have had to make sure our guests and family drink safely and have subsequently become experts (I use the term very loosely) in Ph neutralizers, filtrations units and UV light treatment. All of this is used to either add alkaline to our very acidic spring water so the copper pipes didn't corrode and turn our hair blue, or remove bacteria without the use of chemicals. Not a cheap way of filtering but it meets the regulations and we get to keep our great-tasting water without a whiff of chlorine.

With the exception of power, post and dustbin collection, we are pretty much left to our own devises in this part of the country. Being too far away for mains water, gas or drainage can mean costly investments. Investing and learning about biodigesters for sewage treatment, solar panels to supplement the electricity supplied to the holiday cottages and treatment of serious wet rot in the cellar gave way to an interesting start. So much for the 'simple life'.

The initial house and cottage developments took the best part of 18 months and left us with absolutely no money at all. We did the best we could on the budget we had and relied heavily on two areas of expertise to get us through.

The first was a grasp of figures. Making choices with an understanding of a balance sheet is far less scary as the thousands become tens of thousands. It is, of course, completely true what they say about budgets, double it and you may come somewhere close to the reality.

Secondly, this was my third house project with my husband, and his seventh. We knew enough about it all to know that it was going to be a year or more of non-stop decision-making, living with builders (thank goodness for the outside loo) and a perfectly even layer of plaster dust on every single surface. We hadn't factored in the added stress of having two young children hanging around the house – but despite it all, we managed to come through it alive.

Contrary to stereotype, I hate shopping. I'm not over-keen on queues and too much choice overwhelms me, so taking on responsibility for the entire interior design and purchasing of all necessary furnishings for three cottages was nothing less than painful. If you're going to share your environment with paying guests, whether that's a farm shop, training courses or accommodation, it's always best to share nicely!

BACKGAMMON

Cottages furnished with items that have clearly been moved out of your own home, purchased because they're cheap or chosen with no care as to whether they suit, does not go unnoticed by visitors. The task was made even harder by the fact that we had inherited many things from the previous owners and had brought a mountain of furnishings with us from previous cottages. As is always the case, you replace one or two things in a room and the rest looks tired and suddenly very old. Sometimes it's easier to start from scratch – and that's exactly what we did. Out came the old kitchens, carpets, taps, lighting, crockery and a wall from each of the two smaller cottages.

When the work on the accommodation was finished after only three months, we still had the dilemma of six very useful skips plonked, quite literally, in the middle of the yard. The tractor tyres, chemical containers and copious tonnes of concrete were yet to be removed from the otherwise reasonably attractive drive. Who, in their right mind would want to stay here?! All three cottages had needed total refurbishment. All three had to start paying for those costs as soon as possible.

Although we had eight years' experience of running five-star holiday cottages, they had never been a primary focus as we juggled them with full-time careers. This time was different. Opening the farm up to the public would influence our choices as we wanted and needed to take guests into consideration, especially if we wished for them to return.

Pick Your Own Veg

Sections that might have been used as storage for us would have to be used as a laundry room for guests. We turned a disused gravel section into a beautiful shared patio and barbeque area, partly under an old 15th century byre for shelter. Newly-planted beds in the garden were created to grow cutting flowers for guests' cottages, and entire herb and vegetable plots were built especially for visitors to pick from.

Having always been very passionate about creating a welcoming environment, we wanted to give those who had chosen to come and stay with us the opportunity to be as much a part of this life as they wanted to be. Guests will not necessarily enjoy stepping through slurry to get to the car or being woken at four in the morning by milking machines, so deciding on which animals to keep, and where to keep them, was imperative.

Although properties like these are never really finished, we were finally equipped for the first part of our business. The holiday accommodation business could start to grow alongside the smallholding dream. It was going to be up to me to run it, develop it and get stuck in to as many smallholding activities as I could. Our plans, ideas and preparations for the future of the farm reminded us that the journey had really only just begun.

Chapter Three

Chickens, Pigs and Kids

I have grouped these under one chapter because in many ways they require the same things – food, water, love, cleaning and lots of outside space. The fact that one eats lasagne and cooked broccoli and the others eat it raw (alongside feed purchased in 25kg bags) is irrelevant!

Growing up in the countryside, whether that's upwards (children) or outwards (pigs), requires a great deal of staying power and independence. This way of life is a busy one. Everyone has to muck in.

A long time before children or Middle Farm came into our lives we had kept an eclectic mix of chickens – a variety of rare breed bantams clucking around the garden, enjoyed for their beauty not their miniscule eggs! Sadly, after a fatal fox attack on our first night here, we lost every one and decided to invest in 'normal-sized' rare breed chickens. This way we could supply our cottage guests as well as our own larder with a delicious mix of different coloured eggs that were worthy of a decent meal.

The place that was to be the chicken pen at Middle Farm was littered with tyres, old chemical containers, glass, rubble and bits of metal. Not a playground for the kids and certainly a distant reality from the grassy plot that we needed. With help from friends, a digger, 85 tonnes of topsoil, a post-basher and plenty of fencing materials, we cleared it all in the space of a few weeks, sowed the grass and protected our new investment with a high, sturdy fox-proof fence. 'Digging in' chicken wire to over a foot beneath ground, whilst retaining plenty of height above, is not an easy task – but worth the effort if you're to deter the hungry predators.

I remember returning home from work one evening many years before Middle Farm to a garden lawn strewn with feathers and very dead but uneaten chickens. The indescribably horrific carnage left behind by the mindless killing machine that is a fox is enough to remind any chicken keeper not to skimp on fencing.

A significant budget was spent on wood for building a huge hutch. Inside, a crisscross network of our hazel branches dipped in wood preservative made for perfect roosts, suitable for hundreds of chickens. For us, the importance of space and quality husbandry meant we filled it with only 22 little eight-week-old pullets.

It was going to take a while for the eggs to pay for themselves, especially at a rate of only six a day, but many of our favourite rare breeds were included, from the exceptional 'five-toed Silver Grey Dorking' (an aggressive little madam who has no friends and quite frankly doesn't deserve any!) to the stunningly attractive and very elegant 'Chamois Pencilled Friesian Fowl'. Others include various Marans, Light Sussex and Welsummer, beautiful breeds that lay different coloured eggs including the deliciously dark brown ones (Welsummer and Cookoo Maran).

A powerful but unruffled Buff Cochin cockerel also had his place here on the farm for several years. Aptly christened 'Winston' after a cockerel-naming session on Facebook, he played his part in fertilising many eggs

and helped maintain a certain discipline among the girls. Cockerels can be very useful if you're introducing a new gang of youngsters to your collection and want to avoid too much fighting. Watching Winston care for, feed and protect his harem of hens whilst 'strutting his stuff' around the yard often reminded me of the alpha male qualities in our own species!

We have always found chickens easy to look after and maintain. Whilst we avoid giving them meat products, they eat most of the scraps from the kitchen; vegetable peelings, uneaten sandwich crusts and leftover pasta to name but a few. If they spot you carrying a bowl outside they'll assume it's for them and run, at great speed, to make sure they don't miss out on the day's treats.

We'd spent years filling chicken feeders with cut maize and mixed corn and wondered how so few chickens could eat so much grain. We finally learned, however, that throwing their feed out onto the grass twice a day saves a fortune by not feeding all the neighbouring pigeons, squirrels and crows! Chickens eat all the grain they need in the morning and before bed. A rich protein diet makes excellent eggs, so despite the risks, we let them wander around the acres that surround the house during the day. Partly to improve the quality of their diet as they gorge themselves on worms, bugs and any other delicacies they can find and partly because we (and our guests) love to watch them aimlessly mooching. Since they can't see in the dark, they return to roost before dusk ready for lights out and lock-in. Best not to let them out (at all) if you're going to need them back in again way before it gets dark – rounding up chickens is a time-consuming game!

Many of our girls have proven themselves to be very self-sufficient and, left to their own devises, make competent mothering hens. On missing bedtime lock-in for three weeks (assumed dead), we were astonished to see Marjorie return home with a cluster of fluffy multicoloured chicks. It's so much easier when they do it themselves, no need for incubators, turning of eggs, supervised hatching or cleaning out – just a mothering hen, a thick undercarriage of feathers and access to food and drink. Luckily for them, they all turned out to be hens. We keep the hens. For as long as they lay scrumptious eggs as often as they can and don't turn into cockerels, they are safe. Of course they don't really 'turn into' cockerels but some breeds can be difficult to tell apart until you hear the fateful 'cock-a-doodle-do'.

Children – our own and cottage guests – adore collecting the eggs. The forager in all of us can't help but want to count and collect the goodies at the end of each day. But between careless handling from the kids and pockets limited to five eggs, I've learnt to take a basket. We even have offers to buy the chickens. Only on one occasion did an Ecuadorian tribal chief ask if it were possible to purchase a bird to eat… there's not much meat on an egg-layer so they all survived another day.

When we decided to grow a few turkeys for Christmas, the chickens coped very well with their new, albeit transient, friends. Although they started off the same size, a few months down the line the chickens were clearly perturbed by the giants that were dominating their pen.

MIDDLE FARM EGGS
MIDDLE FARM EGGS

The day came to deal with turkey number one. We'd prepared ourselves by watching YouTube videos on the most humane 'kill' methods. Turkeys are very big strong birds so we needed to have a plan and know how to execute it – literally. It worked. I wouldn't describe it as one of the unsurpassed moments in smallholding but I found myself thanking the bird for its life and wishing it well in turkey heaven. It may sound a bit daft but I have come to understand that rearing any animal for meat, especially if you are responsible for the physical act of ending its life, heightens your appreciation and respect for it. For me it always feels right to be grateful. Keeping chickens and turkeys has also been a great way for our children to learn the balance of life and death. As an adult smallholder this has been an interesting learning curve but it is remarkable to watch how our youngsters have accepted this without difficulty.

That same turkey was going to be our first home-grown Christmas bird and was hanging, ready to be plucked in one of the outbuildings. Our son, aged three, walked in and asked immediately what it was. The answer was a truthful one. He then wanted to confirm that it was the turkey that had been in the chicken pen only an hour before. He became interested in plucking and then followed it through to the kitchen sink still wanting confirmation that this was the same turkey. Once gutted, cleaned and refrigerated overnight, he still needed to know that it was the same bird. The next day, Christmas Day, the turkey was dressed, cooked and served. Confronted with his plate of food he asked one last time, "Is this the same turkey that was in the chicken pen, the one I saw in the shed with all the feathers on". "Yes" we both said together. He then leaned over his plate, kissed the meat and said "Thank you turkey". Then promptly gobbled it all up. Pardon the pun!

Children can be remarkably robust. The truth is much easier to accept if you don't know any different. The same applies to keeping pigs and eating sausages; we know where they come from, the children know where they come from. The relationship between kids and animals on a farm changes instinctively when they (the children) understand which ones are for breeding and which ones are for meat.

Unlike chickens, we did make a very determined effort to learn about pig husbandry well in advance of them coming to the farm. I distinctly remember how horrified my friends looked to hear that I'd been given a pig-keeping course for my birthday. They were, of course, blissfully unaware that my husband and I had been exchanging gifts found at an agricultural merchants for years, so the idea of a pig-keeping course seemed positively romantic. I'm not sure if I was more excited about the five-hour journey with no kids or the prospect of spending the whole day being introduced to every pig breed available in the UK, but that day changed everything.

For me, happiness is definitely pig-shaped, and after two years of begging, it was finally agreed that we could welcome our first trio of British Lop pigs to Middle Farm. We decided on this breed not just because they are British and the UK's rarest, but, unlike other rare breeds, they do not go to fat easily. They are scarce partly because they do not look particularly distinctive and are easily confused with the Welsh or Landrace; but as a traditional breed they have a thick skin which allows for arguably the best crackling ever tasted! They make delicious pork as well as bacon. Not all breeds are duel-purpose so it is worth researching if you're planning a purchase. They're also very docile, lovely natured, great mums and grow to be nicely-sized pigs for pork or bacon weight.

Raising the first three weaners (eight-week-old piglets) on the farm was a hugely rewarding experience. They were small enough to be transported in the boot of a truck. They remained unnamed for pork reasons but were much admired, cuddled, fed and watered by the whole family. The farm finally felt like a farm. As soon as we had 'proper' livestock we knew our smallholding journey was going to be an interesting one.

In true 'new to pig farming' style we made them a sheltered area within the cattle sheds out of straw bales and a heavy marine ply lid. We honestly thought it would be the perfect cosy house for our new little weaners to snuggle up in. And it was…for about 6 weeks. You can never underestimate how much pigs love straw. By the time they were four months old I had to patch up the 'house' with new straw bales on a daily basis, their shelter knocked down and eaten by boisterous boars.

It was great fun putting into practice some of the lessons learned on the pig-keeping course, in fact the entire system that encompasses keeping farm animals. Feeding rules and advice, health checks and understanding how our smallholding CPH number suddenly had a purpose. Without it, I could not bring the pigs onto the farm. We were allocated a herd number needed for transport but there was still a lot to learn about registering and setting up animal movements – all done online. Tagging, tattooing and loading animals onto a stock trailer were all part of the learning curve. According to the farmer next door I'm a natural at 'tagging', not sure if this is a compliment yet. Using a pair of large scissor-shaped clippers to puncture a sharp-edged steel tag through a pig's ear for identification purposes is not one of the highlights of pig farming but imperative for transporting.

Getting friendly with pigs destined for the abattoir is not wise. It's on a par with letting them nibble your wellies when they're

young. There comes a point when you wish you hadn't. Pigs are very friendly and will show affection if you let them. In my experience all piglets love to nibble wellies, and it's very cute when they're only a few weeks old. Entering a pen of ten six-month-old pigs all trying to nibble at your boots is less cute and actually quite dangerous. My greatest dread of pig-keeping is finding myself flat on my back and surrounded by snouts. It would be at that moment I would discover if they really would eat me!

It took me a while to get used to the hideous smell of their wee but needs must. Mucking out pigs is fabulous exercise and another reason I didn't feel the need to renew the gym membership. It is hard work but I enjoy the hugely cathartic feeling that comes over me as I watch them play with their new bale of straw and bedding. It lasts approximately thirty seconds then it's time to move on to the next job.

At nearly six months old and after a delicious diet of grass cuttings, garden leftovers, unsalable supermarket veg and good-quality pignuts, the time came to take them on their final journey. We knew that we couldn't have given them a better life but I was curious as to how it was going to make me feel. With the help of some incredible neighbours, I managed to tag their ears, entice them into the trailer, turn the key, and drive, very carefully, the 25-minute journey to the small abattoir at the back of Griffiths butchers.

It was a very exciting day. Learning to reverse a two-wheeled stock trailer proved almost laughable as the site requires all deliveries to be backed in off the main road – practice makes perfect (lots of practice)! Meeting, for the first time, the characters that I have come to know quite well at the abattoir was fascinating; they even took the trouble to let me know when the pigs had been dealt with – I hadn't even signed the paperwork and so was relieved to hear it had been so quick and without stress. I was, however, surprised to feel a sense of pride and achievement rather than any sadness or guilt. The point at which your pig becomes pork is very gratifying; you know unequivocally where your meat has come from, the life and the death. That is what makes it so special.

On returning to the empty cattle sheds it was clear that we had to make some changes to our pig housing. Our cattle sheds are 100ft long and made up of two equal sides with a raised middle driveway between the two. We use this area to store feed, straw, barrows and farm equipment, but it is essentially the route to feeding the animals, whether cows or pigs. There are giant doors either end to restrain heavy weather and a cattle barrier on each side of the driveway. As the name would imply, these sheds were designed for cows and needed much attention before we could accommodate lots of pigs. Giant doors with an 18-inch gap at the base and cattle barriers wide enough for a weaner to escape through would not do. Galvanised steel gates with stock mesh at the bottom and more steel mesh along the cattle barriers has, so far, kept most piglets in the right pen. Although pigs love mud, some firm ground such as the concrete floor of the shed helps keep their trotters healthy and stops them spreading. Although already under the cover of a shed roof, pigs do need somewhere cosy and out of the wind to sleep. Since straw bales were clearly out of the question I went about designing some foldaway, heavy-duty housing that has proven to be the perfect model for us.

Made of marine ply, it bolts onto the floor, is sturdy enough to be used as a scratching board for even the largest boar, and the lidded roof lifts back and fastens to the vertical steels that hold up the shed. The design allows us to flat-pack the entire sty for easy cleaning and avoids the horrendous crouching position needed to replace bedding in a standard pig ark.

Commercially raised pigs kept in sheds the size of ours may house as many as 150 pigs each side. We ordered four. We planned to eat two and keep two gilts (girls that haven't had piglets yet) for breeding. Before they even arrived our shed had undergone an enormous makeover. Our newly designed pens were sectioned off with large spaces for mums-to-be, mums with piglets (in need of a heat lamp), growing weaners for pork and of course, a boar. With no pigs actually in the sheds yet the work continued outside too.

Large holes cut through the walls of the shed and an appropriate area fenced off outside meant they would all have space, straw and access to mud. Pigs are incredibly strong and love to bury their noses deeply into the ground, so super-strong fencing is highly recommended, preferably with a strand of barbed wire at ground level all the way round to stop them digging out the posts. The good-sized snout of the British Lop is a giveaway that no stone will be left unturned. In fact, stones from two or three feet underground will be raised to the surface.

Finally I was able to collect my new gilts Jenny and Gwen and bring them back to live and breed on the farm. A few months later we heard of friends selling their beautiful sow Mabel. How could I resist? Then only a few weeks after that Charlie came on the market. All of them were registered British Lop pigs, three girls and one boy. Middle Farm was definitely evolving.

Deciding to breed an animal rather than just fattening it for meat takes smallholding skills and experience to another level. Firstly, it means facing winter.

There is a good reason why most pig-keepers buy weaners to fatten up during the spring. Keeping pigs, or indeed any livestock, during winter quickly removes any romantic notion of this lifestyle. Lugging countless buckets of water to thirsty animals several times a day takes its toll. Frozen pipes are one of my worst dreads. Except in particularly mild winters, it is inevitable that for three weeks or more each year the water will stop refilling the drinkers and daily routines have to change. The already-frantic school run becomes a stressful nightmare as it has to accommodate the extra 'just popping out to feed the pigs' time. Half an hour or more can be taken up filling drinking troughs under the deafening creaking sounds of frozen sheds. Being prepared with the right vessel does help – pigs are strong and will upturn most things unless either too heavy or bolted to the floor. Leaving the farm for more than two hours at a time is difficult when no water is flowing. Pigs drink a lot and will need refilling regularly. When the thaw finally arrives it's the same feeling you get when you start to feel better after an illness – relief and ecstasy that life is returning to normal.

Secondly, breeding pigs means becoming familiar either with boars or artificial insemination. We chose the boar! With him came a new-found respect for the pig. Being confident with the animals you keep is essential, and pigs are no exception. Making the decision to breed was probably taken far too lightly given our lack of experience but there is ultimately only one way to learn. After nearly breaking my hand trying to restrain an upset sow, jumping fences to avoid being lacerated by boar tusks and trying to control my shaking whilst injecting a sow's open wound, I have learned that some boars are safer with tusks removed. A pig crush (a metal restraint that the pig walks into, that is locked or roped either end to prevent pig from turning, biting or running off) is essential. I have also learned that pig dope does not make them sleepy for long and a good vet is worth their weight in gold. No pig course in the world can prepare you but the steep learning curve plateaued out and we now enjoy every minute of making sure our pigs have the best lives they can, whether they're for breeding or not.

The British Lop boars we have owned have been, not surprisingly, much larger and stronger than our breeding sows. After the loss of our first boar 'Charlie' to old age and injury this breed is unlikely to move from

its position as the UK's rarest with only around 50 boars of its kind. It is a great shame that they are not more publicised as, despite their size and weight, they can make a perfect breed for first-time pig-keepers. A giant boar collapsing against my legs in total ecstasy during a good back scratch or, better still, an oil massage was not what I expected from pig-keeping but you never know what you're going to get! The large lop ear makes it difficult for them to see, consequently they're very docile and easy to manage, unlike some naughtier pigs with pricking-up ears, excellent visibility and 'escape artist extraordinaire' tattooed on their ears. I have the cheeky Tamworth in mind as I write this. I have learned, however, never to go into their pen without talking or singing so they don't get spooked. A charging or flighty boar is not funny.

We replaced Charlie with Ben and on his first day he managed to crash through the stock fence and help himself to one of my girls on heat. The poor thing couldn't run away fast enough as he chased her huffing, puffing and grunting with his corkscrew willy ready to perform the deed! Yes, if you've never seen one before be prepared to be amazed. I was so embarrassed I had to leave the sheds.

On returning an hour later 'she' looked exhausted, filthy and in need for a good brush down. 'He' was in a satisfied slumber calmly stretched out like he owned the place.

How on earth could I plan piglets throughout the year if I couldn't even keep them apart with fencing? Boars do need to be worked, which is partly why so few pig-keepers want to own them. As well as our three breeding sows we hire Ben out on regular 'sex holidays'. That way he stays active and fertile and whilst away he earns the farm a little money too.

After a gestation period of three months, three weeks and three days (followed by the obligatory 3 glasses of wine to celebrate) there is nothing quite like welcoming new life to remind us why we value it so much.

It is always a considerable privilege to sit with a sow in labour and my first experience of this was with our favourite, Mabel, who ended up having 14 little monsters. She taught us that pigs do make nests before giving birth and this is indeed a sign that tiny trotters are on their way. We celebrated new life, an arcane glimpse of it at its most vulnerable and most perfect for the first time. Mabel continues to be an incredible mother and extraordinarily gentle sow, coming to call like a pet dog!

The constant interest in what we do on the farm reminds me regularly of the enormous curiosity that still exists for this way of life. Guests always ask questions about pig-keeping and breeding and many have enjoyed being witness to new piglets or even helping us move them around the farm. Children staying with us have drawn pictures or written stories as part of their summer holiday homework – always about the pigs and chickens!

Smallholding is an education; it removes most of the cotton wool and regularly presents us with tragedy and beauty in a way that only nature can.

I remember witnessing Mabel give birth once to 16 piglets then quite deliberately standing up and sitting down again on top of four of them. I was horrified and did my best to encourage her to stand up. Surely she could hear them squealing? Looking at me from underneath her ears it was as if she was trying to make me understand that she couldn't possibly feed them all. She knew what had to be done otherwise the surviving

piglets would suffer and it would drain her of more than she was capable of giving. Between the 'fight for survival' and 'survival of the fittest' it is not always easy to know what to do.

On a different occasion, Jenny had her first litter. It was my husband's birthday and two days before he was due at hospital for his prostate cancer operation – an emotional day, an odd day. We wandered the half-mile down the road to the local pub for lunch and returned to see ten very restless piglets, seemingly unable to get any milk. At already four-hours old we wasted no time calling the vet and an urgent visit was arranged. Things did not look good. Jenny was in terrible distress, aware that it was not going well, made worse by her loathing of injections; and she required three, one of which would hopefully release the milk supply within half an hour. It didn't work. We tried to suckle the piglets on Gwen who was also milking her own litter but they were immediately rejected. We borrowed a neighbour's lambing bottle and milk powder in a vain attempt to get them to drink an alternative. The vet prepared us for the worst and didn't recommend that we breed from Jenny again. I cried that night. The hard realities of farming, the waste of life and needless suffering coupled with the fear of what was facing my husband less than 48 hours later.

After all attempts had failed to rescue the little piglets we left them with their mum. It felt the right thing to do – no more human intervention, no more stress, they would snuggle up together.

Before the children woke, we made our way to the pig sties with heavy hearts, ready to remove the tiny bodies; but on approaching, the distinct sound of a newly-born piglet echoed round the shed. It didn't seem possible that one of them had survived but the sound was unmistakable. I shall never, for the rest of my life, forget that overwhelming moment, in fact more of a belting reminder to never give up hope. All ten piglets had miraculously survived the night. Already visibly stronger, mum was calm and milking well; they were going to be fine. I cried again.

Growing piglets on the farm comes with the same ups and downs as raising kids; sweet to look at but born to test the boundaries. Many piglets have nuzzled their way under the barbed wire and escaped into fields or other pigpens, and even interrupted guests having a cosy barbeque under the byre. Naughty, curious, welly nibbling monsters that always seem to win the hearts of any farm visitor. Upturned sods in the garden and black faces are a sure sign explorations have been taken to the next stage. Always hungry though, mum's 'grubs up' grunting call has them galloping back under the wire in no time at all. I have to admit, there is a part of me that loves the naughtiness. Watching piglets jump and turn 180° in the air in sheer delight or play hide and seek with their siblings reminds me that the sods are easily repaired.

There is nothing more satisfying and hilarious than letting the grown-up pigs out to roam in open space. Ears flapping like wings as their legs carry them at great speed off into the distance. The 2.5-acre field that surrounds the fenced off pigpens is the perfect stomping ground but there are two important rules; the first is no mixing of families or sows from a different bloodline. Pigs can and will fight each other to establish dominance. This can be to the death so we avoid it completely. You have no chance of splitting them up if they decide to attack. Secondly, a few hours at most; the mud to grass ratio changes rapidly with big pigs in a field. Unless you're happy for your entire land to look like a quagmire all year round it's best to limit playtime.

Raising children in this environment, or watching someone else's enjoy a day on the farm, is a tremendously uplifting experience. Their understanding of the natural world and all the local creatures in it surpasses any knowledge that I had at the same age. In fact, I continue to learn from them all the time.

Stress levels have subsided significantly since we first moved here. Trying to cook supper with two small children in the garden, drawn magnetically to the 'deep enough to drown in' ponds was almost too much to endure. Coupled with the broken glass, chemicals and sheep dip, it took a long while before I could properly relax and know that they understood the boundaries of their new environment. As it has turned out, they are much tougher than I sometimes give them credit for as their freedom to explore has helped them build their own confidence in the world around them. It is not until I witness them coping with city

life that I realise how much our choice has prepared them only for the country. On a trip to a Birmingham theatre for a birthday treat with three young girls, I wasn't sure whether to laugh or be concerned when my daughter sat down on the escalator (or exit-later as she called it) for the ride! After being told to stand up for fear that her dress would be churned up she promptly held her arms out and twirled round with excitement as if she'd been given a part in The Sound of Music. The overwhelmed country kid in New Street Station had us embarrassed and laughing uncontrollably but was a reminder to 'get out' more.

Although computers and televisions still play a balanced part of our lives, true excitement is still found in the discovery of caddis fly larvae under a rock in the stream, or watching newts, toads, frogs or water boatman in and around the pond. In winter, as the foliage dies back, we find a multitude of plastic miniature wild animals and dinosaurs that have role-played in children's games with all the bugs and butterflies throughout the summer. Thankfully, it has finally been understood that caterpillars, dead flies and fleas are not welcome in the house, even if they are in a lidded box!

I am sure that our kids will not fully appreciate the childhood they have here until they are fully grown and maybe have children of their own. When they look back and remember looking after piglets, collecting kindling, making nettle soup in the garden and having acres of space to run, learn to ride bikes and make camps to their hearts' content, I hope they will value the independence they've been lucky enough to grown up with.

It is a very special and privileged way of life that offers them the freedom to make choices that will hopefully enrich their experience of life elsewhere, be it town or country.

Our cottage guests often comment on the beauty of the farm and surrounding countryside as well as the freedoms for our children. It is true, we found a treasure, but I also believe that beauty comes from watching our responsibilities grow in a safe and happy environment. Our chickens, pigs and kids have plenty of space to flourish. They are well looked after, not overfed, and all have a freedom that goes hand in hand with quality of life on a smallholding.

Griffiths

Chapter Four

Pork Lovers

The same day the paper came out I received an email. It was a pdf of the article that had gone to print, a picture of me holding several copies of my new children's book and a delightful write up alongside it with the opening words 'A PIG farmer from the south Shropshire border has written her first book – after reflecting on the experiences of her animals'.

Shock! Still struggling to come to terms with the title 'author' it would appear I could officially consider myself a 'PIG farmer' too. I liked it. It is, after all, a part of what I do. But what had happened? In less than five years Middle Farm had cultivated a reputation not only for beautiful self-catering accommodation and working with local foodies, it was also home to 'Mabel The Pig' (main character in *Mabel's Surprise*) and provided outstanding pork to those in the know.

The food focus developed slowly at first, largely inspired by our guests. At four miles to the nearest shop, taking delivery of pre-ordered homemade delights from our local delicatessen was a delicious way to start welcoming visitors to the farm.

After months of tasting, talking, drinking, meeting, emailing, photographing and experiencing some of the best local artisan produce, the idea of the 'Breakfast Pantry' was born. By ordering many locally-produced goodies – from jams, bread and apple juice to granola and porridge – I had enormous fun putting together an enticing gastronomic package for our culinary-enthusiastic guests. Further still, a food-focused website, including links to specialist cookery courses and mouth-wateringly fine restaurants, saw our gourmand clientele start to grow. I was heading deeper into the delicious world of food and artisan producers, not realising that in no time at all I too would be considered one of them. It wouldn't be long before I would be adding Middle Farm bacon and sausages to the eggs already available in the pantry.

The day I had decided to keep a few British Lop pigs I couldn't have anticipated the impact it would have on me and the running of our farm. Breeding pigs means selling pork. Selling pork means building a reputation, preferably a good one! Breeding pigs with provenance, cared for in comfortable and safe conditions, attracts buyers who care about where their meat comes from. This was going to be the beginning of an exciting foodie journey for me, and indeed for the Middle Farm outbuildings!

At the end of my long day learning about keeping pigs, all those fateful years ago, the course owners cooked up a whole shoulder of Tamworth for the class participants. Up to that point I knew two things – one, I loved pigs, two, I hated eating pork. In my experience it was usually dry, tasteless with next to non-existent crackling. But that shoulder of a rare breed pig was in no way comparable to the poor relation I had known as pork for the best part of nearly forty years. Like many things in life, once you've tasted 'the good stuff' it's difficult to go back to anything less.

I didn't eat pork again until those three little piggies we first met at eight-weeks-old grew to the appropriate age and weight. I arranged for the abattoir to turn one half into sausages while I helped my butcher and friend Bert cut up and bag the rest. Most was sold to friends and family and we kept the remainder jointed in our own freezer. The following Sunday we were to taste our first, very own, home-reared rare breed pork shoulder roast. After six hours in the oven, slow cooked to perfection, it was quite simply the most succulent pork we had ever savoured and the crackling… well, suffice to say there was nothing left.

Friends, family and guests alike reported back exactly the same. They could all taste the difference and all demanded more. I was only too happy to oblige.

Within the first year we developed from buying a few weaners for fattening-up to breeding our own just so we could keep up with demand. The interest in animal welfare as well as the flavour of the finished product is a point of paramount importance to our customers, and local support for what we do has been phenomenal from those that know.

Left with no choice but to be carried away with my enthusiasm, my husband agreed to yet another conversion of yet another section of the outbuildings. This time a fabulous and functional storage room emerged. Tiled floor, insulated and ventilated doors, sealed and painted walls and safe electricity for the first time in its five-hundred-year-old history. The lights worked without flickering and four huge chest freezers, two spare fridges, a stainless steel work bench, one thousand half-dozen egg boxes, four portable cool boxes and the beautiful French-styled glass fronted Breakfast Pantry all fitted in with ease. By word of mouth my British Lop pork business started to grow and now we had somewhere to store it.

As I drive into town every Friday clad in the same old recognisable wellies, coat and hat, I deliver all my 'mates' pre-ordered frozen bags of sausages, chops or pork joints for the weekend. The power of Facebook and Twitter have undeniably contributed to helping me promote the farm. The cottages, the animals, the produce and daily working life all feature but it is also the medium for many of my friends to see what we have in stock. By Thursday evening my Facebook private message box is jammed packed with pork orders, some insisting that their kids won't eat any other sausage! Who needs marketing when you have a group of ten-year-olds doing the job for you. It has been suggested that I need a new 'brand' name. These vary in vulgarity but 'Sam's Sausages' is repeatable enough. Nonetheless, their support of small farmers like me is crucial to our survival and having direct contact with our customers in this way makes it so much more entertaining.

With the farm several miles away up in the hills it makes sense to deliver weekly to our keen supporters in the town.

This public Facebook message from one good friend is a firm favourite and makes all my efforts worthwhile:

"Oh 'Sausage Queen', Oh 'Sausage Queen'
I need my pork-based fix
Is it possible you could furnish me
With a simple string of six?"

Selling any product when you have faith in its quality makes it an easy job but selling half-pigs has been an education on several fronts.

I owe my local butcher, Bert, a lot more than just the value of all the chopping, sawing, boning and tying that he has done for me. Together we have butchered and bagged more pigs than I care to count. All cut differently to meet the requirements of my customers and labelled appropriately for the freezer. Cutting up animals is not for the faint-hearted (unlike the chainsaw accident, I'm fine with butchery on dead things). Half a pig weighing at least 25kg requires enormous skill and precision if it is to be cut and boned well, wasting as little meat as possible and keeping all fingers attached to the butcher's hand. Being involved in this part of the process had taught me an enormous amount about all the different pork cuts and joints. In turn, I can (and do) pass on this knowledge to my consumers. Half-pigs can be difficult to imagine if you've not had the privilege of cutting one up, and many will

Rebecca - 18 sausage
2x Bacon
12 sausage
35 reserved
Teresa

be put off buying if they think that a piece of meat the length of their sofa is going to be delivered to their door!

Friends of mine who breed organic Longhorn cattle suggested using loaves of bread as a guide to the size of freezer space needed. I think this is the perfect measure. Half a pig looks like eight or nine loaves of bread in size, although weighs considerably more. Further still a diagram goes a long way to help potential customers understand exactly what it is they are buying:

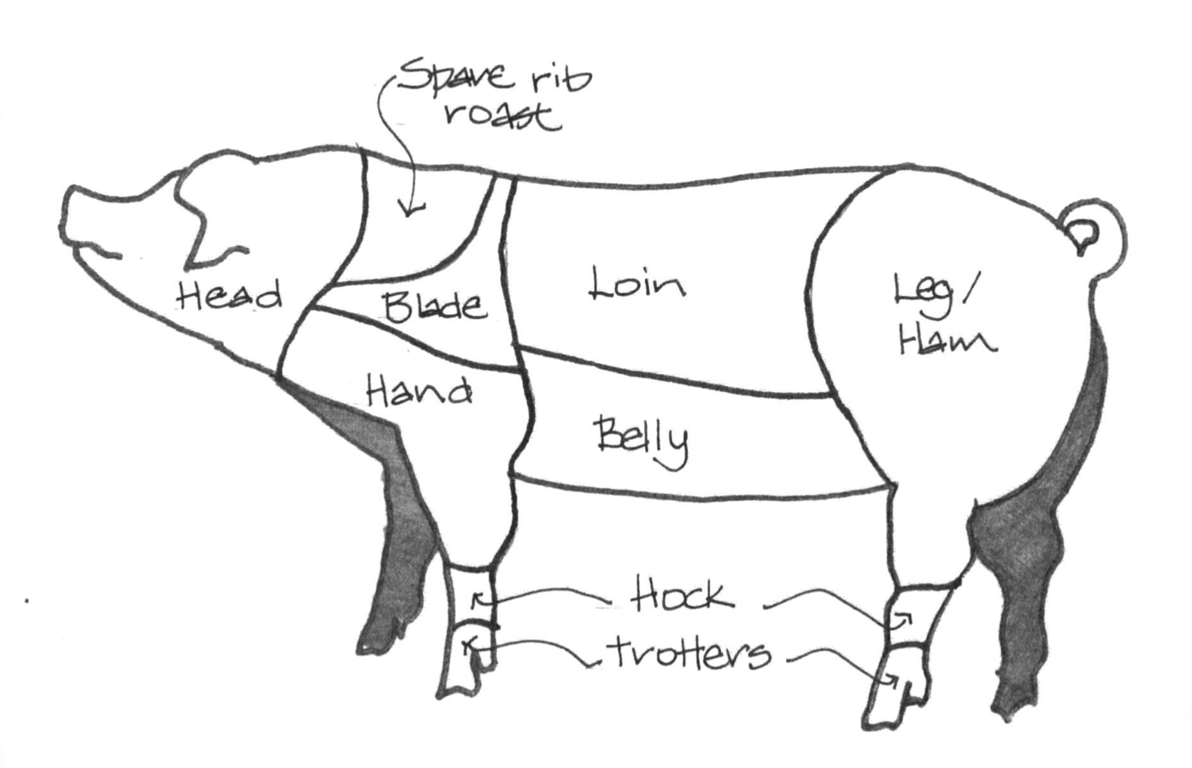

The reserves for a half-pig are now increasing. Chefs and other food-loving friends fuelled the demand by making fabulous comments, tweeting mouth-watering pictures of cooked pork and kindly donating (in the case of chefs) their own pork recipes for our farm website.

Although trade grew enough to warrant setting up as a registered 'Food Business', investing in trade scales and labelling equipment, display refrigeration unit and tray wrapping and sealing machine, we were both mindful of keeping the 'small farm' status. There are two main reasons for this. Firstly, we'd lose our point of difference if we grew too big. We have no intention of cramming our outside space or sheds with hundreds of pigs. We want our guests and pork customers to visit the farm and feel better about eating our produce. The knowledge that they have had a good and happy life should and does make a difference.

Secondly, pig farming is not a particularly profitable business. They did warn me about this on the pig-keeping course but my selective hearing was in overdrive after cuddling a few newborn piglets. It's true that every time I do the accounts for the pork business my heart sinks a little at the pathetic return for the work involved. In fact, if I factored in the hours of labour spent cleaning, loading, transporting, butchering, preparing for freezer, selling and delivering pork, the losses would be exorbitant. So how and why do I do it?

How? I completely ignore the time invested. For me those hours don't count. I'm a smallholder and I don't pay myself a wage but if I did I wouldn't be able to afford to keep pigs. I am, however, very disciplined when it comes to pricing. Keeping the value of the pork at the right price is imperative (another lesson I learned on the pig-keeping course and through my experience in sales). Trying to compete with commercial standard pig breeders by selling high-quality rare breed produce at less than it is worth is not only financial suicide but it undervalues everything that makes small pig farmers different.

Rare breeds are special and should be treated as such. Rare breeds kept in deluxe conditions (for a pig) with plenty of clean straw and space makes for happy pigs not cheap pork. My experience has led me to develop a market directly with my supportive customers rather than butchers or restaurants. It may be easier to go directly to sellers or chefs initially but (depending on the outlet) after they've taken their own margin the loss in profits can make it unsustainable for the producer. However, different chefs have different budgets and putting a rare breed at the right price on the menu for just a month or two can be very beneficial to both the restaurant and pork supplier.

Why do it at all? For the love of the pigs and all that they bring to the farm. Despite all the labour and effort involved in keeping them, they are the main attraction for many of our guests. They make Middle

Farm feel like a farm. Their personalities and sometimes extraordinary behaviour is hilarious to watch. They have, without knowing it, educated us on so many levels. Not only in the experience of raising them but as a constant reminder of why provenance and breed matter. I believe this goes for all animals – sheep, goats and chickens alike.

Raising the profile of Middle Farm pork has required careful consideration. We only have a maximum of sixty pigs a year available for pork. Mabel, Ben, Jenny and Gwen are not ready to become bacon any time soon! However, it is alien to my nature to turn down opportunities, so when I learned through Twitter of a new Food Festival opening on my doorstep it was the perfect opportunity to say "Hello, I've got pigs and pork – can I come please?!"

I went to the meetings, filled in the forms, made the calls and sent the emails, and somehow the idea of a pig roast developed into 'bringing a sow and piglets to the first ever Shrewsbury Food Festival'. I had never been to a food event where livestock were present but what better way to remind people, both children and grown-ups, of where their food comes from.

I realised quite quickly after starting to breed the British Lop pig that I was less interested in 'showing' them at agricultural fairs and was developing a keener interest in educating people about animal husbandry alongside the taste of exceptional pork. It is very gratifying to be able to talk to guests and friends about the breed before they leave with a cut, joint or several sausages.

All being well the festival was going to be an opportunity to show piglets, sow and pork on a much grander scale than we had been used to. After a few hurdles with local by-laws, the council pulled out all the stops to get a CPH number for the chosen plot of land. For the first time in living memory there were to be farm animals in the central parkland of Shrewsbury town, known as the Quarry. My Jenny, with the same ten miraculous piglets born nearly four weeks before, were to spend two days and one night in a cosy pen being spoilt rotten with attention. Next door would be a stunning Longhorn Cattle cow with her calf, also being doted on by crowds of animal lovers.

The twenty-day farm shut down rule meant that I couldn't bring them home and then back out again. Unless an animal is being moved for slaughter, 'movement restrictions' prevent any other animals to come and go until maximum incubation for swine flu or any other disease period is passed. In the case of pigs, that is twenty days, so they had to stay in the Quarry overnight.

A few days before the food festival I started to have those 3am panic attacks. How was I going to load a very protective sow and ten small piglets in time to get them settled in? What if they wouldn't get in the trailer? Would I be able to fit the divider between sow and piglets inside the trailer? What if Jenny broke through it in a desperate attempt to get to her little ones and ended up squashing them on the journey? Nightmare scenarios. By 4am the fears of escape completely took over. Much-needed sleep was replaced by imaginings of my sow and piglets galloping around the Quarry grounds, digging holes under every available bush and tree and completely ruining any chance of a beautiful Shrewsbury Flower Festival to be held in the same place only weeks later!

Answering my pleas for help, three willing farming neighbours kindly offered their expertise and help on the morning of the festival. With a total of more than a hundred and twenty years of experience between us you'd have thought it would've gone without a glitch. But no! Loading small piglets is like herding cats. They ran everywhere except in the back of the trailer and had to be manhandled one at a time. Meanwhile, it was rocking violently from side to side as Jenny went berserk trying to get to them. My middle-of-the-night visions were becoming an early-morning reality before my very eyes.

Three-quarters of an hour later with ringing ears courtesy of the squealing piglets, they were all finally loaded up. As they settled down with the motion of the car, I drove the stock trailer into the heart of town. A neighbour kindly followed to help me unload at the other end but by the time we'd arrived, all tantrums had subsided and had given way to complete compliance. They were all impeccably behaved for both days. Of course they were spoilt and overfed as they grazed perpetually on pignuts and apples from the moment they arrived. Luckily they were unperturbed by the hordes of crowds they attracted, the ooh's and the aah's, the constant flashing from photos and squeals of delight on hearing mum's grunting call to tell her piglets that 'milk was up'! As those ten little piglets started to suckle, many of the grown-up visitors to the food festival realised this was as much an education for them as it was for the children. There were some that found it difficult to equate the animal to meat but most tucked in willingly to the spectacularly prepared Middle Farm pulled pork served by a nearby restaurant manager and friend. In fact, it was so popular they ran out of our meat in under one hour (note to self – have more pork available next time).

Being as cute as they were, the piglets were a huge success and much admired by those who came to take a look. I must have spoken to over a thousand people that weekend. My jaw ached from all the piggy and pork talk. The questions were constant and similar: "How long is the gestation period for a pig?"; "At what age are the piglets weaned off mum?"; "Why are they a rare breed?"; "How old are they when they go to slaughter"? This last question was occasionally followed by mutterings of "Oh no, I couldn't do it… you don't give them names do you?" In the firing line of so many good questions, I surprised myself that weekend about how much I had learned in my two years of pig-keeping. It was an extraordinary experience.

Tiring, yes, but fulfilling to be in a position to pass on those learnings to the masses of people who appeared to care about what they ate.

At the end of that weekend, weary but happy I was relieved to load Jenny and her piglets into the back of the trailer effortlessly. In fact she had a serene glow about her. It was as if she'd understood what it had all been about. She had relished the attention, the oversized food portions, the noise, the chatter, the rest and eight hours a day with me by her side. She and her piglets had been safe and content and we'd spent more time with each other than would ever normally be spared at home.

It wasn't until a few days later that I learned of the mark we had left behind. I don't refer to the hundreds of people that tweeted, messaged and emailed about how much they had enjoyed seeing piglets at a food festival but the enormous hole that Jenny had rooted out in the grounds of the Quarry. With the straw and fencing removed the damage was quite shocking in the otherwise beautifully kept grounds. With some replacement soil and grass seed the organisers of the show put right what Jenny destroyed and even invited us back the following year.

I hope the future of our pork selling business will be at many more local food festivals as well as the continuing 'Friday drop-offs' to longstanding supporters. I don't think there is a greater privilege for smallholders like me than to be able to demonstrate the food cycle from 'farm to fork' in this way.

(How we cook our pork)

I've always found it quite amusing that so many of my regular customers turn to me for ideas on how to cook pork. Not amusing that they should ask but amusing that I should know. A few years ago my knowledge of pork and pigs was zero and here I am being asked advice on how to get the best crackling!

I am not a chef and would never profess to have a mass of experience when cooking pork in different ways. Actually, in truth I am a bit of a coward. The thought of possibly ruining a beautiful piece of meat with anything less than a good, long, slow cook, allows me to justify cooking it in (almost) the same way every time. With the exception of pork balls, chops and tenderloin, I slow-roast all cuts and joints.

There are hundreds if not thousands of recipes available for slow-roast pork, each with their own take on herbs, vegetables or any other additional ingredient. But for simple folk like me achieving unbeatable crackling and succulent meat is of the highest priority and the following page explains how I make sure I'm never let down.

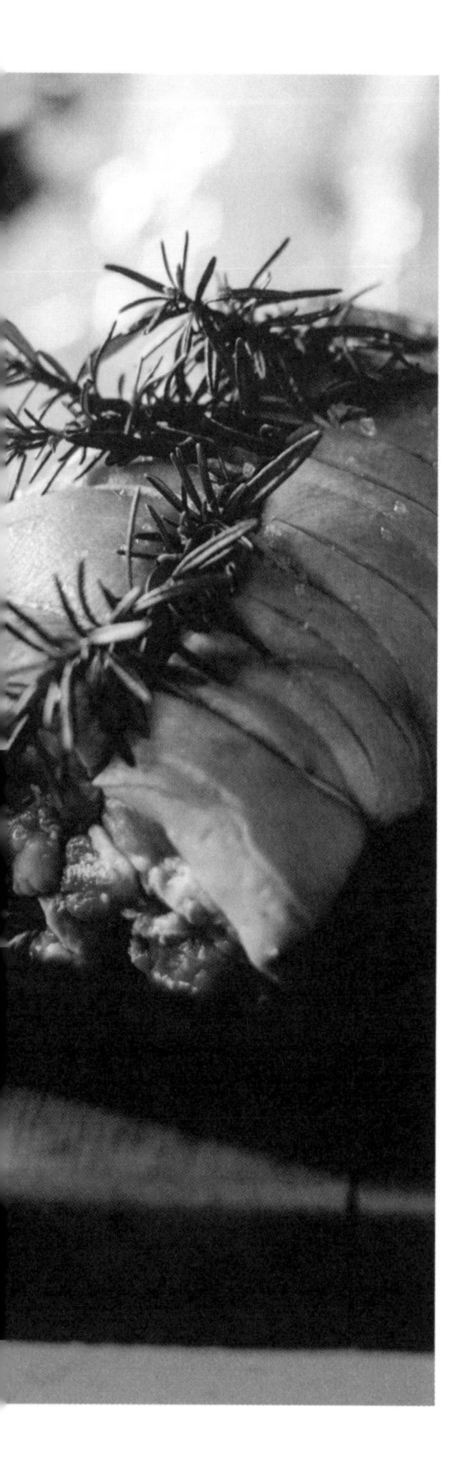

With the exception of leg, I slow-roast dry. That's just a personal choice.

Heat the oven to around 200°C salt the pork, leave it uncovered and when it goes in the oven turn it down to 150°C. Roast until skin is brown. This is usually around one hour. Remove the pork and put a double layer of foil snuggly over the top. Put back in the oven for 30mins/lb. Then remove the foil and place in the oven for another hour until crackling is firm and crackly!

For the leg, we always roast with a liquid. It is a hard working muscle and liquid stops it from drying out. I like to slice lots of apples and place at the bottom of the roasting dish, salted leg on top then fill with a mix of cider and stock up to around two inches deep. Slow-roast as mentioned above. Top up the liquid every so often to make sure it doesn't dry out.

Then serve and enjoy in the knowledge that any leftovers make equally great meals, hot or cold.

JOSEPH BENTLEY

Chapter Five

Getting Down and Dirty in the Veg Patch

To write this chapter I have a special chair. It is battered, worn, completely uncared for and would probably look more at home on a skip. However, it offers me two important comforts. The first is somewhere to collapse with a hot mug of coffee, out of the wind and the rain, irrespective of how filthy I am. Secondly, although it sits haphazardly in the greenhouse, it has a wonderfully inspirational view when writing about fruit and veg.

Growing vegetables from seed is, for me, one of life's greatest pleasures. Even the thought of sowing seeds sends a calming through me like

no other. Yes, it requires time, nurture and knowledge, but it gives an abundance of edible delights, the quality of which is rarely exceeded by anything shop-bought. It is my treat every year on Boxing Day to sit down and plan the veg planting for the following spring. That may not be as exciting as hitting the sales at 4am, but it's far more appealing to me. It never ceases to amaze me that every year the same things are repeated – purchasing seeds, preparing ground, sowing, watering, then watching

– and those first green shoots always send a spark of excitement through me, totally disproportionate to the event. The cycle has begun again. Do all vegetable growers feel the same excitement? That primeval instinct to cultivate a skill that teaches us to feed ourselves?

I was nearly 27 years old when this 'instinct' started to invade. Slightly unsure about what to do, I reluctantly tuned into Gardeners' World every Friday night. However hard I tried to suppress it, I couldn't help digging up our old garden, learning about various composts, seeds and all the paraphernalia that goes with becoming a vegetable grower. With a birthday in spring, thoughtful friends and family made sure spades, trowels, specialist books and gardening gloves were never in short supply. My executive, slightly cool party-going image was in tatters, but luckily it mattered not. My husband patiently stood back and watched as I slowly cultivated a little more of our plot each year. While he has no interest in sowing and growing, I dare not total the hours he has spent helping me shovel manure, build beds, rotavate clay soil and generally offer his man-power. His only payback for all this work has been plenty of delicious vegetables, probably the most expensive available if 'time invested' were factored in!

There is no fast-track to becoming a successful vegetable grower. Every year presents itself with new challenges, sometimes weather-related, sometimes disease or a particular pest and sometimes it's just a lack of knowledge. I once nurtured my first ever butternut squash seed, it was the only one that germinated so I looked after it very carefully. After a couple of weeks I thought it looked a bit strange for a squash, then all was revealed... my father fell about, unable to speak for laughter at the care and attention I had given to a baby bindweed.

This is how it goes, year in, year out, learning new things. Over the years I have tried to live by the lesson that there is always next year; next year I'll remember to net against cabbage white butterfly before their arrival, sieve the soil for large stones before planting root crops, shoot and eat the rabbits or invest in some wire fencing, grow mainly beefsteak tomatoes as I find too many cherry varieties a pain to pick. Then, next year arrives. Shrewder than the year before and prepared for all the nasties, I find myself speechless at the deer that have leaned over my newly-erected rabbit proofing and devoured every sweetcorn planted.

No one said it was easy but it gives us an appreciation of just how hard it is to produce any crop without the chemicals or super-protection enjoyed by commercial growers.

On a smaller scale, a greenhouse is an excellent start. Without it, we would have very little to eat from our land. The small wooden 8x6 version in the garden at Middle Farm offered protection for the first year or two here. I crammed as many full seed trays as I could onto the rickety

wooden slats that made up the only surface, then struggled for space when they needed potting into much larger containers. Needs and ideas soon outgrew their limitations, so a new plan was put into operation. The task of building a 22x12 greenhouse at the back of the yard proved far more complicated than first expected. As with all constructions, a flat surface was required, so digging and levelling began. It should have been simple but the unseen and unknown ancient drainage system underneath the hard core surface suddenly gave way to liquid clay. The hired dumper truck disappeared almost vertically into the ground with our 'mate' still in it. It was one of those moments when you're not sure if it's appropriate to laugh as his head peered out at soil level. It took two tractors totalling 170 horsepower to pull him out and an hour-long pressure-washer (another Christmas present) session to clean the machine down.

A polytunnel would have been much easier but the high winds up here would have meant regularly replacing the cover and permanently picking out the blown-away plastic sheets from surrounding trees and bushes. Greenhouses this size can be in excess of £15,000 so we chose the simpler and much more affordable route of paying a carpenter friend – with access to treated cedar but no experience in building greenhouses. Amazingly, it worked! It took nearly a year (on and off) to complete and probably isn't as hi-spec as many on the market but it survives the high winds and is the perfect cover for all newly-sown seeds and growing plants. Luckily the ancient drainage system was filled in with more concrete hard core so the new glass and timber construction should be staying above ground for a while longer. Evenings spent working in the greenhouse during the last remaining light of the summer months are hard to beat. With the children, chickens and pigs all tucked up for the night, the contrast of a refined glass filled with good red wine against hands covered in sowing compost seems to sum up my life as a smallholder. For me, greenhouses are a special space – light, warm and full of goodness. They are quietly calming yet bursting with life. They offer something to snack on during many months of the year, making them a delicious retreat, perfect at all times of day and in any weather.

Alongside the greenhouse, but far enough away not to block out the light, we dumped several tonnes of very well-rotted manure. It was a fruit bed in the making, to be filled with summer and autumn raspberry canes, gooseberries, blueberries, blackcurrants, redcurrants, blackberries and a rhubarb that seemed to find its way there by accident. It is possibly the most delicious part of the garden. It was also my first solo post-bashing experience. Oddly, I felt a sense of gratitude as my husband duly passed me the post-basher, directed me to the fencing wire and tightening devise and happily left me to get on with it. The fact he didn't feel the need to help me erect the 18 fencing posts used to support the raspberry canes, or wire them up, gave me confidence that I'd get them straight enough. Building strong supports for canes

is crucial if you actually want the fruit to flourish. Apart from the lack of light under a straggly mess on the ground, they'd otherwise be eaten by every mouse, squirrel and chicken that can reach. Since we're not the only ones that enjoy grazing in the fruit beds, the next tactic is to build a cage around the supported fruit to keep the birds off. I have to confess, I didn't get that far. My theory is to pick the fruit before they become sweet enough for the birds, otherwise we share.

The other side of that same fruit bed is full of kindly-donated blackcurrant bushes. Eaten directly from the bush, blackcurrants are outstanding and the instant shot of vitamin C is unquestionable. However, anyone with more than two bushes will know that to pick them all and process them is highly time-consuming, especially in a good fruit year. We have seven highly productive plants and in true smallholding style have always imagined making copious jellies, ice-cream, cordials and other bottled delights. I even convinced a good friend, who popped round for tea, that blackcurrant picking together wouldn't be nearly as back-breaking as it sounded. Once inside the house with our six kilos of fruit it became obvious that no muslin square I owned was ever going to be big enough to strain this mountain of berries. Even if it were, it would take days! Over the years I have made all of the above-mentioned treats but admit that the preferred option now is to pick as many fruit as possible, stew in a little water, strain through a small meshed sieve, add icing sugar to taste and freeze. Total time spent, including picking: 1½ hours. The kids love the sorbet and it can double up as a delicious coulis if you freeze in small batches and strain the seeds when needed.

Time spent preserving, pickling and freezing is an important part of smallholding life; after all, the idea of living off the land is why we do it. However,

Early rhubarb jam

I have to confess, it has taken me a long time to stop feeling a failure when it comes to harvesting and preserving in huge quantities, i.e. large enough to last the year round. All the books and manuals I read before becoming a smallholder spoke of delicious recipes and methods used to preserve the fruits of the land, both wild and cultivated. They enticed me into that world of natures' harvest and allowed me to dream of a life picking and conserving, at least for a few months in the year. What they failed to tell me was how to juggle this with the laundrette run, cleaning out the animals, cooking the kids' tea, taking pigs to slaughter, dealing with bookings, garden, school run, finances etc. etc. Living this life is more than just a 'try to do' list, there are things that have to get done or people and animals suffer. Harvesting fruit and veg is hard work and often labour-intensive fruits all arrive at the same time; elderflower, gooseberries, rhubarb and of course blackcurrants. This is the point at which I try to remember 'there is always next year'. And the truth (in my opinion anyway) is that no one can do it all. It'll be a long while before I even attempted making butter, soap or beer. In the meantime, we eat all that we can when available, conserve in quantities that suit us and give plenty away to grateful friends and guests.

On the topic of fruit, however, my 'little' greenhouse never went to waste. One of the greatest gifts you can give a smallholder is a tree and for one big birthday, several years ago, I was lucky enough to be given a peach. An unusual choice for British climes, not least of all given our high altitude and propensity for deep snow and ice. I can't imagine many folk up here in the hills eating their own home-grown peaches, but that rickety glasshouse turned out to be the perfect frost protector. Admittedly, the branches have to be trained around the edge and when the leaves are out there is little room to move, but it works. Our prolific little tree gives us hundreds of peaches every summer. Luckily, they're not good in jams! But they do make great crumbles, delicious packed lunch fodder and are the ideal accompaniment to a bowl of breakfast muesli.

Unlike fruit, all vegetables at Middle Farm were to be sown from seed. Before we could do so, whether inside or out, we opted to build a large number of raised beds. I had learned from previous experience that maintaining a mass of open cultivated ground is mostly a muddy mess and makes weeding a back-breaking nightmare. I'd never used raised beds before so it was a bit of an experiment. They were made using a treated soft wood, ranging in length but never more than five-foot wide for easy reach. The 25-year-old cow muck at the top of Sunny Bank, scooped up using the tractor, was used as the majority filler and the remaining space was filled in with topsoil from the veg garden surface. It took all summer for the garden lawn to recover from the tyre marks but the raised beds looked magnificent. Cow muck retains high quantities of water so stops the soil within the bed from drying out too quickly. Keeping on top of weeds is a difficult enough task during the warmer months but the beds helped as these plots are undeniably easier to maintain – a highly recommended investment. Making weed-free pathways wide enough for a wheelbarrow between each one, covered either with gravel or paving stones, is another worthwhile luxury.

Once the beds were finished, the propagation plans could begin in earnest. Given my passion for sowing I prefer to grow everything from seed rather than buying plants; a personal choice that doesn't necessarily mean better flavour but does offer greater varieties. The greenhouse starts to come alive with the germination of those first seeds. Trays and

trays cover the entire work surface, full of squashes, melons, cucumbers, peppers, tomatoes, brassicas and any other variety that needs a little warmth to get going. It is at this point that the work and the watering begins and gets progressively more intense as the season goes on. There are two very important lessons that I am still learning; the first is grow what you like to eat. That may sound obvious but most growers, myself included, are easily seduced by beautiful vegetables or grow what they think will look good in the garden. That's all very well, unless the family don't like purple cauliflower or leeks. Secondly, be careful of quantity. I was justifiably proud one year of a bed full of well-formed celeriac, but after eating five, six, seven, eight… I was less sure how we were going to munch through 65 of them.

By the time summer has arrived, we can pick at least seven or eight varieties of vegetable for every evening meal. It is an incredible feeling to pop to the end of the garden and collect all that you need to feed the family, over and over again for several months in the year. Within that time the selection available changes from spinach, salads, peas, beans and cucumbers to root crops, brassicas, leeks, squashes, tomatoes and peppers. This is a part of smallholding that I truly love and hope to be doing until the day I die.

The work involved is irrefutable. On top of weeding, staking, netting and harvesting, a dry summer can involve hours of watering. This can be particularly stressful if rainfall has been low and our private water supply depleted. I have been known to take a few buckets out of the pond rather than draw fresh water at peak times. In more abundant years, our children have proven themselves to be a little help in this department. A love of water and mud ensures that most of the veg are reasonably nourished or sometimes drowned. I also encourage them to grow a few of their own seeds in some of the spare clay pots. They duly water them and are equally excited when green shoots poke their heads out – although lots of thinning is required as often 800 carrots are sown onto a surface not much bigger than a diner plate. Nevertheless, gardening in this way is a great excuse to be outside for most of the summer. Afternoon snoozing in a sun-lounger is a long and distant memory but the effort made is more than worth the produce repaid.

Much of the veg grown here gets eaten as it ripens and the rest is often fed to the pigs. Courgettes the size of marrows, runner beans over a foot long, broccoli with yellow seeds, you get the gist. There are, of course, many veg that store very well, either in the ground or in a dark corner somewhere that you mustn't forget about when you need to scrabble around for enough potatoes to feed twenty people. After watching many onions and garlic rot in what we thought was a dry carport, we decided to invest in converting the end of one of the old barns into a potting shed. It didn't require a huge amount of work as the stonewalls and lack of light served perfectly as a dark, dry storage room for these said veg.

POTTING
SHED

Copious bundles of garlic and a variety of onions can now hang from the walls to dry; bags of potatoes sit waiting to be eaten alongside harvested carrots, that can in fact be stored for several months; and next years' seeds dry out and are kept for the following spring.

One of my personal favourite root veg is beetroot; it needs no protection, except possibly from mice (raised beds help), it stores well in the ground for months, is easy to pull out without a fork, is incredibly versatile in the kitchen and we all love the taste. Actually, that's not entirely true. The children love the fact that eaten in large quantities it turns your pee pink! So a well-known recipe for beetroot and walnut hummus is a regular in our house, even as a Sunday lunch served with flatbread and green leaves from the greenhouse. Busy weekends often mean easy lunches straight out of the garden (followed by pink pee).

The winter veg are, in my opinion, the best reward for the year's work. It takes that long to witness your purple sprouting broccoli finally develop edible florets or for the curly kale to recover again from the caterpillar attack earlier in the year. When you find yourself digging up parsnips, carrots, beetroot and leeks by torch light at 4.30pm for a roast veg concoction to be served with melted goats' cheese, it shouldn't matter that the kitchen sink is full of mud and foliage. It is almost more rewarding than the summer months because you're still feeding off the land in the depths of winter and the flavours are just as good, if not better.

Growing greens, particularly brassicas, has got to be one of the hardest groups to get right. It would please me no end to see the kids as enthusiastic about the curly kale and sprouts as the slugs, birds, chickens, mice and caterpillars are. The minute you take those little seedlings out of the greenhouse the battle for veggie survival begins. Without decent butterfly netting you may as well not bother, but it is worth the effort. Purple sprouting broccoli is a must-have on our plot. It was eating this vegetable within half an hour of cutting that I first noticed the difference in flavour. Some crops are much more affected than others by the time lag of 'plot to pot', and this is one of them. The taste is like no other broccoli available, not even someone else's home-grown as long as you eat it soon after cutting. Carrots and potatoes straight from the ground are unbeatable but the quality of home-grown winter greens is far removed from their distant relatives found in gassed bags in the supermarkets.

One of the downsides of growing such appetizing delights in the garden is the sacrifice of time spent on other, less edible parts.

We inherited, from the former owners, a beautiful cottage garden, stunning plants and flowers growing in organised chaos with bursts of colour all year round. As winter turned into spring and then into summer we realised the enormity of what we'd taken on. While my attentions had been on the vegetable gardens it turned out the inconspicuous network of bindweed and ground elder, running their roots underneath every single flower bed, had done their best to take over. Carefully submerged amongst the roses, lupins, peonies and many other typical cottage garden plants they suddenly seemed to raise their ugly heads and demand an incongruous amount of work. Even during our second winter here, when temperatures dropped to -19°C and we lost approximately an eighth of the garden plants, as well as all the newly planted shrubberies, even then the bindweed and ground elder survived.

Feelings associated with the garden vary from person to person. In my view, it is a place of therapy and relaxation even if the work is heavy and the weather unkind. It gives me time to think, reflect and cherish the lifestyle we have on this farm. That day, when we were late and lost trying to find Middle Farm, was only one week after my mother died. It hadn't been a particularly long battle with cancer but within four days of her passing we learned that the original sale of this farm had fallen through and it was now back on the market. I was at my father's house at the time and he insisted we look on the website. Excitedly searching for

something else to think about he turned to me and said "You have to go and see it, this could be it Sammy". He was right. To this day and forever more, in my gardens of time and reflection, I will always imagine this place as a very special gift. In doing so, I plant daffodil bulbs every year for her somewhere in the garden, always a different variety and always as a reminder of her favourite flower.

Caring for a smallholding is very much about connecting with the land, and the garden offers the perfect place to do so. Although it requires work, I hope that it will never become stressful. Allocating small chunks of time, taking one area at a time, is the way I try to approach what can sometimes feel like an overwhelming task.

If I had more time to manage it I would gladly make the whole garden edible (apart from the daffodils), but as it is it remains a true cottage garden; and a beautiful floral display, with the network of bindweed bothering me much less today than it did.

Investing and building a new set of raised beds for our guests to pick from during their stay with us has been hugely successful. They can enjoy, in the same way we do, the freshness and flavour of newly-picked vegetables but without any of the work. We do not charge them for produce taken but we trust them not take it all in one go. Needless to say it is a very seasonal offering. In winter there are herbs, greens, stored onions, garlic and potatoes and in summer we grow the most popular of easily picked veg, such as beans, mangetout, courgettes, various green leaves and carrots. Access to the greenhouse means tomatoes and cucumbers are also in plentiful supply. Knowing guests buy our pork and cook our vegetables to go with it is deeply fulfilling as they can appreciate the taste, convenience and work involved in all areas.

While the initial investment in growing any vegetables may take some time to pay back – depending on choices made, of course – the rewards are even greater than the flavours of 'home-grown' produce. The fundamentals of smallholding are at work in a vegetable patch. Growing them alongside the pigs with equal passion and perseverance is not easy, but putting them together on a plate, even in simple form such as bangers, mash and purple sprouting is an instant reminder of why we chose this lifestyle.

Chapter Six
Giving it up for Wellies

As I write this book I reflect back on the dreams that were. Various television programmes that, when put to beautiful music, seemed to intensify our desire to give up our secure careers and take a risk. Books written by those already living the smallholding life would put a funny slant on stories and again encourage us to throw caution to the wind.

I understand that many good smallholders start off inspired by the same dream. After years of commuting to work through relentless traffic, making do with processed sandwiches for lunch, endless meetings about targets, results and, ironically, 'personal development', it's not hard to understand how and why so many of us become disenchanted with our everyday business. It does seem a little extreme to 'jack it all in' for a life looking after animals and growing your own food, but for all the different reasons – be they independence, fine tuning survival skills or just wanting more space and being more connected to nature in our otherwise hectic existence – I can say with experience that for me, the reality has surpassed the dream.

On moving here we would occasionally refer back to the files we had compiled during our life 'before wellies'. While surrounded by the initial turmoil and building work they reminded us of why we had moved in the first place and kept us focussed on the end goal. I can admit that, at the beginning, there were times I would drive by a charming old Victorian town house and catch myself longing, just for a second, for a manageable garden and a house that wasn't permanently cluttered with wellies and straw.

As the dream became my reality, the enormity of what we had taken on and the opportunity for our future started to really sink in. Slowly, one day at a time, we substituted the files for the real thing.

Smallholding means different things to different people. For some it may be a few acres of land with vegetables enough for the summer months, a dog and a horse and a slightly dilapidated greenhouse; for others, several tens of acres filled with the full works – chickens, pigs, goats, ponies, cats, dogs, geese, bees, vegetables, fruit... and the list goes on. Whatever the dreams and aspirations, I have learned that, for me, the utopia of total self-sufficiency doesn't really exist. Although it can be an attractive concept for many people buying their own land, the reality, of course, is that we all need each other or at least 'some' others to survive. Unless you have volunteers or employ help, there is simply not enough time to do it all. By far, it is better to do a few things really well, trade with those that produce other things you need and develop slowly so you can learn and manage as you go along.

This lifestyle choice comes with many responsibilities, especially where animals are concerned – their welfare has got to come first. The consequences are that some sacrifices have to be made. In our case and I'm sure for many others that do the same, it is 'time'. Time spent outside the farm. I don't refer to delivering pork or the school run followed by the occasional coffee with friends, but quality time – time to take a day off walking in the hills just because it's glorious outside or opportunities to be out and about with the family. We do try and make the effort to go to special places as a treat but it isn't often and I occasionally question whether the kids suffer as a result. If there were a list of 'things you must do by the age of ten' they would probably fall far short of their non-farming mates. It's difficult enough to hide the groan I feel inside at the suggestion of an after-school activity let alone anything that may eat into our busy weekends as well! Then I watch and I see how much they absorb from the world around them, a world completely alien to many of their friends and I feel absolved of any wrongdoing or deprivation. They are far too busy making up games and feeding their imagination to be concerned about what they're missing. Besides, they have their lives ahead of them to fill those gaps on their own terms. In the meantime, they'll have to muddle along with us and the irregular town or city visit.

Farming on any scale, especially when it includes livestock, generally limits spontaneous weekends away to 'never' and well-planned escapes to 'very occasional'. Our one week away per year, usually within the UK just in case we need to get back for guests, has been, for many years, the extent of our annual holidays. Luckily we love Cornwall. To be honest, by the third night away my husband and I are already hatching plans of what we're going to do on our return, such is the inspiration of new surroundings. By the fifth night we're itching to get home and put all of our ideas into action.

These yearly excursions have to be planned months, if not a year, in advance so as to arrange someone to feed and water the animals, plants and vegetables, take care of any guest needs and make sure the house isn't empty for long. My sister has been a great filler of these shoes – it's seen as a break for us and a break for her as she and her brood adore the smallholding life for that one week a year. On our return I usually find a pile of cash for the all the pork chops and sausages they've munched their way through, a list of all the non-urgent telephone messages, the garden weeded and the ironing pile neatly pressed and left on the beds. As if we would charge her for pork!

On a rare weekend away to London recently, my husband and I were struck by how our senses felt extraordinarily bombarded. The visual stimulation between Kings Cross and the hotel left us completely exhausted. Having lived and worked in London in bygone years it reminded me of how and

why city life can be so stressful. I had just never realised by how much. Throughout the normal family chaos of our daily lives it is often our guests who unknowingly remind us of how lucky we are to live in this environment. By making comment on the stars at night, the lack of any traffic sound and the beauty of the countryside, they make sure we never take it for granted. One spring, a guest from central Reading confided in me that, on waking the first morning to the sound of sheep, his initial thought was that his kids had changed his ringtone as a joke! How we laughed as he slowly settled into his week in the countryside and the 'non-virtual' sound of young lambs outside.

We see how our guests' shoulders visibly relax by the end of their break, and often their perspective on life changes entirely, especially if they have been witness to the birth of twelve piglets. These surroundings are conducive to contemplation and relaxation. And that is, for me, what makes smallholding so alluring.

This way of life is not about instant gratification. It does require good foundations, patience and hard work but in return it not only fulfils many empty voids left by 'modern-day living' but it teaches us new and far more valuable skills. Although many friends and guests suggest that they too would 'love to live this life', they are less attracted by the enduring work involved. I can understand that shifting piles of muck, handling farm animals both dead and alive, lugging 25kg bags of feed around whilst permanently clad in tatty clothes and wellies is not everyone's idea of good living. Personally I find it a great privilege, albeit hard work, to spend my days this way. It is not a job. There is no clock off time or weekend break. It is a way of life, a life that requires good health and an inordinate amount of self-motivation. The diversity of things on the 'to do' list is extensive enough to keep even the most easily bored out of trouble. This includes me! Being able to switch from finances and marketing to shovelling manure and collecting pig carcasses makes every day extraordinary.

There are many moments that I catch myself in sheer unadulterated happiness, always provoked by simple things – the first birdsong of spring, countryside sounds that could so easily be drowned out by traffic, a view from the back of the chicken pen, the tell-tale signs of clean air as the lichen grows in abundance.

It is always very saddening to hear or read about smallholdings that haven't succeeded. I cannot profess to know what the exact failure or success rates are but I do know from my own experience that sales and marketing even in the 'good life' are crucial to survival. Good and new ideas are also key – they keep smallholding fun, diverse, alive and always prepared for future changes.

As with any business, there has to be a source of income large enough to sustain the smallholding and the people living on it. Producing a product that has a limited market or that nobody knows about is unlikely to bring in the necessary financial rewards. Running guest accommodation may not be considered a typical smallholding activity but it is the very reason we can afford this lifestyle at all.

The inspiration for writing this book not only comes from observing the environment around me but also the risk of losing it. My husband's cancer came completely out of the blue when we had been at Middle Farm for about four years.

It felt like the pause button had been pressed. We had no idea what was going to happen, would he ever have the physical strength to manage this lifestyle, would our dreams of running a smallholding together be squashed? The unknown was unspoken as we dealt with one day at a time. It was agreed that he would worry about getting better and I would concentrate on the children and the farm. Contemplating the possibility of losing it all was enough to motivate me to start taking notes, which are the foundations of this book.

I would regularly return home from the hospital to find that our neighbours had cleaned out the pigs or friends had arranged to collect the kids from school and feed them tea. This was kindness in overwhelming magnitude and I'm not sure how we would have managed otherwise. It took many months, an enormously painful operation and lots of strength and determination but he finally got the all clear. The relief as we could press the play button was indescribable. A second chance allowed us to take stock and re-evaluate. Were we doing what we wanted to do? Was the reality everything we'd hoped it would be? Faced with the possibility of having it taken away we became even more certain that our choices were right for us. I remember seeing a plaque in a little boutique shop that read the words 'Happiness is somewhere between having too much and too little'. I believe that is true and that this lifestyle offers balance and perspective like no other I have ever known.

As I write this final chapter my husband prepares to leave work. I did what I set out to do and completed the challenge. Middle Farm now turns over all that it needs in order to sustain it and our family. The key is making sure that we always stay forward facing and grow steadily at a rate we can manage.

The future is an exciting place to visit, at least in our heads – plans for a woodland walk, delivering firewood to the locals, more animals, training courses...

The truth has always been that we are perfectly suited to this somewhat rustic way of life and continue to be inspired by Middle Farm much more that we could have imagined.

And so we continue, always on the first day of our adventure, learning new things, changing our minds, going about our daily duties and, not surprisingly, always in wellies.

Wynnstay Group Plc
www.wynnstay.co.uk
25 KG

Outtakes

Acknowledgements

Kate Taylor (Editor)
Richard Hammerton (Photographer)
Bing Taylor (Chairman of Middle Farm Press)
Bert Butler (Butcher)
Adrian (Abattoir)
Stephen and Joy (Farmer, neighbours and huge help)
James (Farmer, neighbour and piglet loader)
Carolyn and Dennis (Cottage guests)
Karon (The blackcurrant picker, garden helper, drinks lots of tea, best mate)
Chris Burt (Chef and Middle Farm pork supporter)

Pork Supporters!

Brian and Amy
Keri NJ
Naomi and Orla
Sue and Sam
Tara and Warran
Marcus and Jenny
Chris B
Will H
Andy R
Colin Y
Julia W
Kerry and Lee
Simon and Drea
Malcolm
Ben and Nicola
Rebecca
Becks
Bridget
Helen
Sue M (always remind to pick up)
Lucy
Sara L
Sara D
Suzanne
Jo
Joanne
Jacob's mum
Sally-Anne
Kate B
Kate and Nick
Kate C
Kate D
Kate S
Kath G
Katie W
Challon
Karon
Emma
Kirsten
Henry
Paula
Ed
Annabelle (South Shrops)
Simon
Hailey
Fenola
Louise
Seb's Mum
Clara
James R
James D
Toad
Claire
Caroline
Bev
Kath
Sally
Sam P
Emily
Natasha
Bing
Alan
Rhiana
Angharad
Denise
Francesca
Victoria